sea turtles up close

Ocean Education Publishing
216 North Federal Highway
Lake Park, FL 33403

Ocean Education Publishing strives to teach and inspire us all to value and protect our natural environment and all wildlife.

Library of Congress Cataloging in Publication data.
ISBN 978-1-4675-0572-7
Printed in China by Everbest through Four Colour Print Group

sea turtles up close

Photography by Jim Abernethy
Written by Jennifer R. Nolan

Foreword by Céline S. Cousteau

Graphic Design by Leslie Evans

Ocean Education Publishing, Florida

*This book is dedicated to the conservationists
who help protect sea turtles, and their environment
at large, and to all those who follow in their footsteps.*

Foreword

When looking at sea turtles I see wise beings—incredible navigators of the oceans, patriarchs of a clan. Like the elders of a village, they seem to hold ancient knowledge, passing on stories and information to the next generation. Traveling water highways with fine-tuned navigational senses and their instinct at the helm, they dodge shark teeth, floating plastics, and now fishing nets amongst a myriad of other obstacles to get to nesting grounds and feeding sites; survival is not a given for these reptiles.

To know that all seven marine species of turtles are now in danger of extinction is a tragic fact. Nature knows best how to create a balance of species with predator and prey in constant motion. One has to ask why all sea turtle species are now in need of our protection. We must seriously consider the destabilizing impact our overpopulated, developing world has on all life forms that inhabit our water planet. We would be wise to make the necessary changes to live in harmony with our natural world.

This is the time for introspection and action. The origin and ingenuity of solutions lie in the very same source as the cause of many problems—humankind. We are undeniably a destructive species and yet we are also an incredibly capable species. We are capable of adaptation, capable of change, able to find the root of issues, and create effective solutions. We defend and protect our own species with such incredible fervor and energy that it is hard to believe we would not do the same for the health of an entire ecosystem we depend on more than we can ever imagine—our oceans. Within these oceans we find incredible sea creatures that have for so many centuries wandered the underwater realm through its blue and green passages. It is imperative that we extend to them our capacity to love, and more importantly, our ability to protect.

By "diving into" *Sea Turtles Up Close*, we learn more about who these beautiful creatures are and how to take action to help protect them. Woven throughout the pages are splendid images by Jim Abernethy— images that bring these noble animals to life and into our homes and hearts, connecting us to them in a personal way. Sea turtles are a reminder of times past and times to come. In their eyes we can see a reflection of our own ability to think, feel, and act. Let's not lose this grand opportunity to do something positive.

Céline S. Cousteau
Founder & Executive Director-CauseCentric Productions
www.celinecousteau.com

1

Preface

Sea turtles, to know them is to love them. Regarded as archangels of the sea, they are possibly one of the most endearing animals on earth. Marine biologists, scientists, and conservationists continue to produce compelling discoveries each year about these unique, resilient reptiles—expanding our understanding for how these animals achieve their impressive longevity, physical prowess, and remarkable navigational feats. In addition, like all animals, sea turtles play a key role in our fragile ecosystem. They are here for reasons beyond our current knowledge, and to study them, or simply view them in their natural habitat, is a privilege.

My first introduction to sea turtles occurred as a young teen when I encountered a female loggerhead emerging from the sea in the moonlight. I sat quietly and watched as she exhaustively hauled her massive body up the slope of the beach in search of a place to dig her nest. Captivated by her determination, I watched her fulfill a primordial mission of immeasurable significance in the night; she was creating the next generation of sea turtles. Once her task was complete and the nest covered over, I witnessed her slip back into the sea and disappear into the underwater world, her home. This loggerhead encounter left an indelible impression on me, fueling my curiosity about this species for a lifetime.

A few years later, I came across what appeared from all perspectives to be a dinosaur's nest. Massive animal tracks leading up the beach left markings similar to those of tractor-trailer wheels. This discovery captured my imagination, and I could only wonder what behemoth created this crater-like depression in the sand. It was the highly respected "Turtle Lady of Juno Beach," Eleanor Fletcher, who revealed to me the answer. She explained it had to be a rare leatherback—a sea turtle so mammoth its nest might be mistaken for something manmade. Fifteen years after discovering that awe-inspiring nest, I had the good fortune of encountering my first leatherback in the wild. At three a.m., one of these enormous animals crawled out of the ocean and somehow managed to heave its body weight of nearly a thousand pounds up the embankment to nest. For some people, seeing this particular species of sea turtle is a lifelong goal.

With their tremendous proportions, dramatic black shell, and unique design—no other animal resembles a leatherback—they are sure to captivate any spectator. Having the privilege to witness loggerheads and leatherbacks carry out these ancient nesting rituals was a moving experience, influencing my life's direction as a nature photographer and conservationist.

For decades now, I have pursued with my camera lens all seven species of sea turtles. Through photography I seek to capture their beauty, behavior, and gentle nature in the hope of inspiring others to join in the efforts to protect these awesome creatures.

While a photographic image can serve many purposes, its greatest value is perhaps best realized when the visual connects people emotionally to a world that is otherwise foreign to them, or when a subject is better understood because of what a photograph reveals. It is only through gaining an understanding and appreciation of a species that one is motivated to help protect them. Jacques Cousteau perhaps framed it best when he said, " We protect what we love."

In the wild, to swim silently alongside a sea turtle, as if in slow motion, amidst the depths of the ocean's blue canvas, is to experience a sacred moment. To hover above one nestled peacefully in a seagrass meadow, or to be present for a hatchling's virgin voyage across a sandy beach, destined for vast, uncharted waters, is to witness a quiet quest to exist amidst nature's serenity and powerful forces. These animals are perhaps best described as simply mesmerizing. Most people will agree, if fortunate enough to witness a sea turtle swimming peacefully, the experience will leave you wanting the encounter to never end.

Their world is our world. We are all connected, and the state of their habitat, and their fate, are indicators of our own. In the words of John Muir, naturalist and founder of the Sierra Club, "When we try to pick out anything by itself, we find it hitched to everything else in the universe." The connection I feel to all marine life inspires me every day to pick up my camera. If these remarkable reptiles could speak our language, what words of wisdom would they whisper? We invite you to look up close, into their eyes, into their world; the answer is there and it's beautiful. Dive in.

Acknowledgements

We wish to thank our family and friends for their endless support during the creation of this book. You are all a constant source of inspiration and love for which we are deeply grateful.

We are honored to have respected ocean conservationist and documentary filmmaker Celine Cousteau contribute the foreword for *Sea Turtles Up Close*. Celine is a passionate explorer and artist whose efforts are making a real difference.

We also wish to express our deepest gratitude to Dr. Jeanette Wyneken and Dr. Mike Salmon, Biology Professors at Florida Atlantic University, and Larry Wood, Conservation Biologist, Zoological Society of the Palm Beaches, FL. Their in-depth knowledge of sea turtles is generated from decades of scientific research and observation, and their valuable contributions to this book ensure we present the most credible data and current insights about these unique animals.

Sincere appreciation goes out to Leslie Evans for her graphic design work. We are honored to collaborate with this talented artist. Leslie Evans Design Associates—ledadesign.com.

Thank you to the photographers who generously provided images. See photo credits at the back of the book.

We wish to acknowledge Maggie Elder (2000-2012), an outstanding young lady who became a cherished member of our "Turtle Team" during the creation of this book. Maggie's love for animals served as an inspiration to us all. We will be forever touched by her beautiful spirit that lives on.

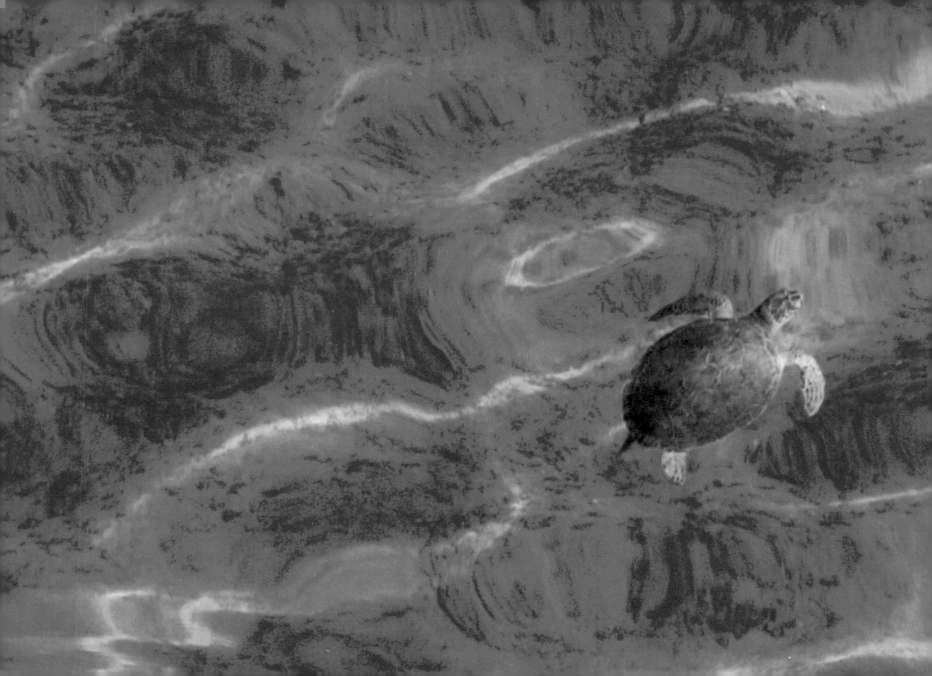

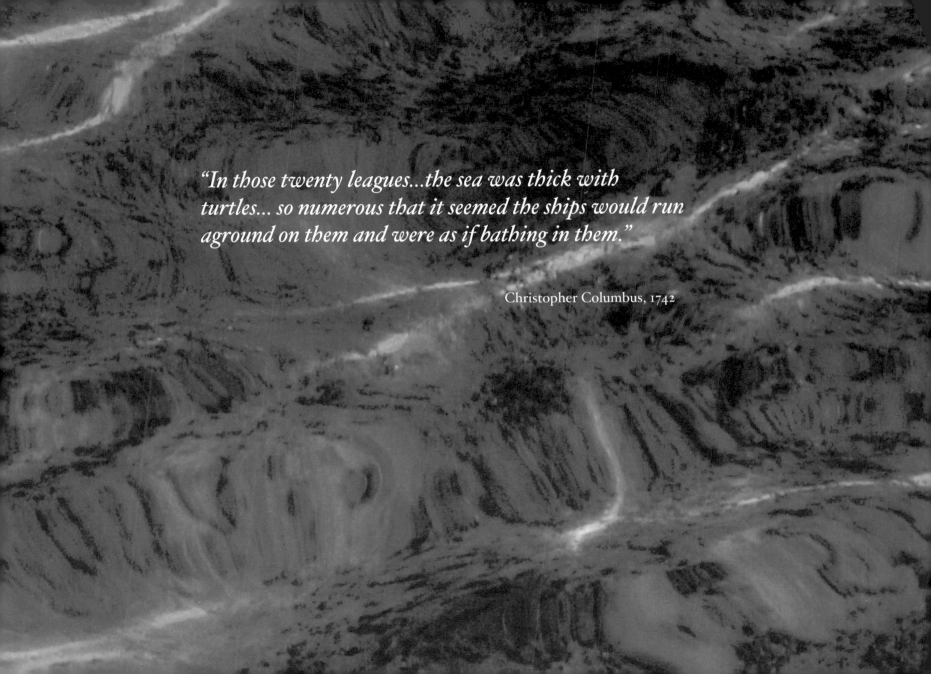

"In those twenty leagues...the sea was thick with turtles... so numerous that it seemed the ships would run aground on them and were as if bathing in them."

Christopher Columbus, 1742

water

What are the differences between a turtle and a tortoise?

Scientists refer to turtles and tortoises as chelonians. Both are reptiles, but turtles live primarily in the ocean or in freshwater rivers, lakes, and streams. A tortoise is a land-dweller, living in grasslands, forests, and deserts. Turtles have a variety of paddle-like limbs for propulsion in water, while tortoises tend to have rounded, sturdy feet with stout toes designed for traction on land. Turtles and tortoises have more similarities than differences, but where they live—land versus water—is the largest defining factor.

land

over **110** million years

How long have sea turtles been swimming in the sea?

The sea turtles that exist today represent an evolutionary lineage that dates back at least 110 million years. They started off as land-based turtles, over 235 million years ago, during the lower Mesozoic Era. These turtles roamed the land and freshwater marshes with the dinosaurs, long before the rise of humanity. Through the course of evolution, their legs took on the shape of flippers, allowing them to swim long distances across the ocean with superb efficiency. Sea turtles successfully adapted to the marine environment—most notably in their hydrodynamic design, tolerance for saltwater, and astonishing lung capacity. An "aquatic life" defines the existence of these resilient reptiles.

What are the different parts of a sea turtle?

BEAK Used for foraging by tearing, crushing, or biting.

BODY CAVITY Occupied primarily by pectoral muscles, guts, heart, and lungs.

CARAPACE Upper side of the shell. Consists of backbone and ribs.

CLAWS Used for tearing food, and by males to grip female during mating.

CLOACA Opening located beneath the tail, where undigested food and urine are released.

FRONT FLIPPERS Assist with locomotion, propulsion, lift, and steering.

MOUTH Toothless with a muscular tongue.

PLASTRON The bottom shell. Joined to the carapace by cartilage and ligaments.

REAR FLIPPERS Paddle-shaped back legs that assist with steering and nest digging.

SCUTES Tough scales overlaying the bony carapace.

SKULL Fused bones protect brain and sensory functions, includes the jaw.

TAIL The part of the spinal column that extends beyond the shell, long in adult males, short in females.

How many different sea turtle species are there?

There are seven species of sea turtles worldwide.

FLATBACK - Natator depressus
GREEN - Chelonia mydas
HAWKSBILL - Eretmochelys imbricata
KEMP'S RIDLEY - Lepidochelys kempii
LEATHERBACK - Dermochelys coriacea
LOGGERHEAD - Caretta caretta
OLIVE RIDLEY - Lepidochelys olivacea

Where do the different species live?

The warmer waters of the planet's midsection provide the most favorable habitat for the vast majority of sea turtles. Six of the seven sea turtle species are found in U.S. waters and beyond; the flatback lives primarily in Australian waters.

FLATBACK: Specific to continental shelf waters of tropical and subtropical Australia and Papua New Guinea.

GREEN: Worldwide in tropical to warm temperate waters.

HAWKSBILL: Worldwide in tropical, subtropical, and warm temperate waters.

KEMP'S RIDLEY: Subtropical and temperate waters of the Atlantic Ocean and Caribbean—primarily the Gulf of Mexico.

LEATHERBACK: Worldwide in tropical, subtropical, and temperate waters.

LOGGERHEAD: Worldwide in tropical to warm temperate waters.

OLIVE RIDLEY: Worldwide in tropical and subtropical waters.

What is the best way to identify the different sea turtle species?

While many sea turtles have similar features, there are a few clues to look for when trying to tell them apart. Consider the difference in size and coloring of the shell and limbs. Note the number and pattern of scutes on the carapace; but keep in mind that some sea turtle species experience a change in color and shape between the juvenile years and adulthood. The scales on the head will also help in identifying each species. A few other things to consider are the shape of the head and shell, and the number of claws on the flippers. Additionally, the geographical location of any given sea turtle will help to identify a particular species.

FLATBACK

GREEN

HAWKSBILL

KEMP'S RIDLEY

LEATHERBACK

LOGGERHEAD

OLIVE RIDLEY

"We protect what we love."

Jacques Cousteau

Are sea turtles dangerous?

Often referred to as archangels of the sea, these animals are known to be gentle, welcoming, and non-aggressive when treated with respect and not threatened. Sea turtles have no teeth or fangs, however, the best advice is: look, but please don't touch. They are keenly aware of their surroundings and pose no real threat to people who come into their visual range. Snorkelers and divers lucky enough to encounter a sea turtle busily foraging, swimming, or resting are wise to enjoy watching these magnificent creatures in their natural habitat.

When underwater, do sea turtles have good vision?

Yes, their vision serves them well. Sea turtles see in color but appreciate a different portion of the light spectrum than humans. Sea turtles also see colors that people cannot see, like ultraviolet light. This helps them locate prey such as jellyfish, which appear transparent to us. These reptiles are expert divers, and scientists have determined that they are in fact capable of seeing at great depths.

Do sea turtles have ears?

Sea turtles do have ears, although they are hard to find. Located on either side of their head, the ears are covered with skin and scales. These animals hear only low-frequency sounds. This is sufficient for when they are underwater but serves little benefit on land. In addition to the ear, the shell may act like a large drumhead and detect some sound vibrations.

Do sea turtles have a good sense of smell?

When underwater, sea turtles have a combined sense of smell and taste. They are able to pick up odors when pumping water in and out of their nose and mouth. When they are searching for food at sea, their sense of smell serves them well. On land, although their sense of smell is reduced, it remains a functioning sensory system. Scientists continue to explore how sea turtles detect smells in the water and wind—there is more to learn.

28

Magnetic field detection—a key sensory system to the well-traveled sea turtle—functions somewhat like an internal compass. This sensory system allows a sea turtle to find its way back to desired feeding grounds, beaches, or the region where it first hatched. This is a place it has probably not revisited for a decade or two.

30

relies on besides vision, hearing, and smell?

From the moment a hatchling breaks out of the eggshell, scientists believe it can sense the earth's magnetic field. A sea turtle's ability to migrate thousands of miles to unfamiliar destinations is considered one of the great wonders of the animal world.

What do sea turtles like to eat?

Most sea turtles enjoy feasting on jellyfish, crabs, clams, snails, horseshoe crabs, sea pens, other assorted invertebrates, seagrasses, and algae. These sea turtles are generalists, feeding on a wide variety of different animal prey. Others are specialists, feeding almost exclusively on one or two things. Dietary habits do vary slightly among species, but they all share one trait, how they feed. Like birds, they have no teeth. Their sharp beaks function like blades, allowing them to break apart foods such as sponges, shells, and seaweed. With maturity, many species become dietary specialists: leatherbacks prefer jellyfish over other prey, greens are like "underwater cows" and graze on algae and seagrasses, and hawksbills exist on corals, sea squirts, and sponges.

FLATBACK - omnivore   LEATHERBACK - carnivore
GREEN - herbivore   **LOGGERHEAD - omnivore**
HAWKSBILL - omnivore   OLIVE RIDLEY - carnivore
KEMP'S RIDLEY - carnivore

" *Health to the ocean means health to us.* "

Dr. Sylvia Earle

Can a sea turtle drink saltwater?

Yes, all seven species have a unique biology that allows them to drink seawater. The salt leaves their gut and enters their bloodstream; it is then removed by salt glands located near the eyes. From there, thick, salty fluids are constantly washed away from their eyes. When on land, this function creates the appearance of tears. In fact, turtle tears are just a necessary process to excrete the salt.

How long can a sea turtle stay underwater with one breath?

The lungs of this aquatic animal have adapted well to life in the ocean, allowing them extended time underwater. This benefits them for many reasons—from foraging to survival. The average time spent underwater for an adult sea turtle, in between breaths, varies based on species, water temperature, and activity levels. Sea turtles typically remain underwater for four to twenty minutes, but elevated stress levels will accelerate their need to surface for oxygen. When asleep, or in a resting state, certain species can survive for hours on one inhalation. Unlike humans who only refill ten percent of their oxygen in one breath, sea turtles can exchange up to eighty percent of the air in their lungs with a single, deep breath.

Why does a sea turtle come to the surface and float?

While a sea turtle will spend most of its life underwater, it will always be drawn to the surface throughout the day for a myriad of reasons. As youngsters, most species "float" for years in sargassum—seaweed found in the central Atlantic region. This behavior is likely an attempt to hide from predators. The need for a fresh, deep breath of air compels all sea turtles to rise from the depths of the underwater world to the surface. Floating also enables them to rest and recuperate after hours of swimming and foraging. In addition, basking in the sun is very common for reptiles—warmth from sunlight helps to raise and maintain their body temperature.

Do sea turtles know where they are going when swimming in the open ocean?

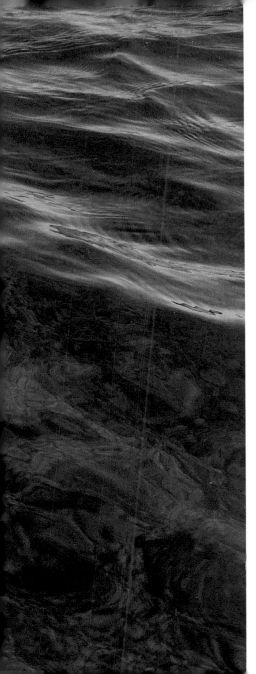

There are many remaining mysteries about sea turtles, and this is one of them. What we do know is that they likely use magnetic field detection, the position of the sun, and chemical concentrations in the seawater to determine their location and the direction they must swim to reach their desired destination. Also, it is possible that these remarkable nomads draw clues from memory of landmarks, oceanic temperatures, currents, and geologic features. So yes, sea turtles are choosing their direction with intention. While scientists have provided some clues, and we know their ability to navigate with "magnetic maps" is superbly developed, sea turtle navigational mastery remains a bit of a mystery; clearly they do not rely on road signs.

At what age can sea turtles reproduce?

Depending on the species and oceanic location, it takes anywhere from seven to fifty years for most sea turtles to reach maturity and reproduce. Loggerheads and green turtles must be at least twenty years of age before they are able to reproduce. Turtles mate at sea while on route to the nesting beach, or just offshore from that site. Miraculously, females sometimes nest at the very beach their mother chose to deposit eggs, or they often select a beach in that general area. Many Kemp's and olive ridley species have a novel nesting ritual—hundreds may arrive at a nesting beach at the same time. This is called an *arribada*—meaning "arrival" in Spanish.

AGE OF MATURITY

FLATBACK 20–30 years
GREEN 20–50 years
HAWKSBILL 20–40 years
KEMP'S RIDLEY 11–16 years
LEATHERBACK 7–15 years
LOGGERHEAD 28–35 years
OLIVE RIDLEY 11–16 years

How many eggs does a mother

The average clutch (eggs in a nest) has anywhere between fifty to 150 eggs and varies according to the species. Nests average sixteen to twenty inches deep (forty to fifty centimeters).

FLATBACK **50-70 EGGS** GREEN **105-120 EGGS**

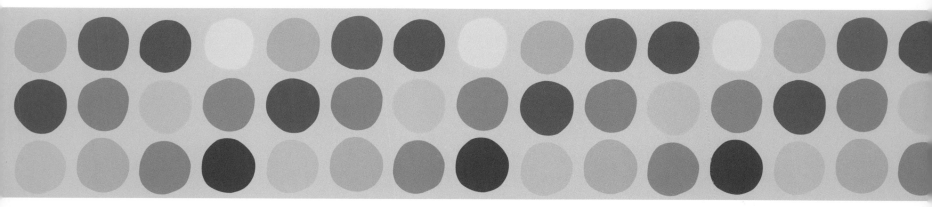

HAWKSBILL **140-180 EGGS** KEMP'S RIDLEY **100-105 EGGS**

sea turtle deposit in a nest?

Eggs have the appearance of ping pong balls and are flexible with a leathery exterior. Scientists have learned that once females reach maturity they will likely nest, but not every year.

LEATHERBACK **70-90 EGGS** LOGGERHEAD **100-120 EGGS**

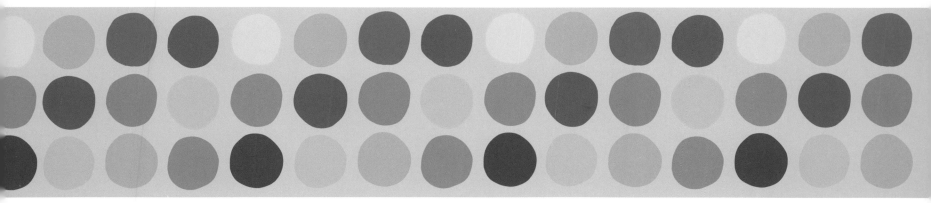

OLIVE RIDLEY **45-150 EGGS**

How long are baby sea turtles in the nest?

Sea turtle eggs need to incubate in the nest for forty-five to ninety days depending upon the sand temperature and species. Once hatchlings break out of the egg, they slowly unfold from their balled-up position. Together, hatchlings work feverishly, digging upward to climb out of the nest, reaching the surface typically in two to four days. If the surface sand is hot from the day's sun, they will wait for it to cool during the night before resuming their efforts. Once free from the nest, hatchlings crawl toward the lower horizon of the ocean, away from the dunes.

Where do hatchlings go once they reach the water's edge and begin swimming?

Once they enter the surf, hatchlings dive to the bottom where the forceful undertow will carry them away from the beach. As they surface to breathe, waves will guide them farther offshore. After approximately thirty minutes, they stop paying attention to the waves and rely on their internal magnetic compass—set by the direction they crawled and swam earlier. Life's adventure has just begun. Until recently, little has been known about the first year of a baby sea turtle's existence. Today, innovative satellite devices make it possible to track their whereabouts. Data reveal that these tiny creatures are great travelers from the day they are born, exploring much of the ocean far from their original beach.

Do most baby sea turtles survive?

ONLY 1
OUT OF 7,000

Unfortunately, no. Out of 7,000 eggs, only one hatchling will likely reach adulthood. Real and constant threats exist on land and at sea—both wild animals and man play a role. In the nest, hungry predators and beach erosion often destroy incubating eggs. As baby sea turtles scramble across the sand in an attempt to make their way to the relative safety of the ocean, they are often snatched up by a variety of predators along the way. By the time a sea turtle matures to the approximate size of a wheelbarrow, most threats have passed—barring large, predatory sharks and fishermen.

Common land threats to hatchlings: seagulls, crabs, foxes, frigatebirds, herons, vultures, raccoons, coyotes, rats, fire ants, and human beings.
Common threats to hatchlings in the ocean: snapper fish, tarpon, mahi, groupers, jacks, squid, and frigatebirds.

What is the largest sea turtle?

Leatherbacks win the prize for size. These famously pelagic (existing in the open ocean) animals are the largest reptiles alive on the planet, weighing in at 550-2,000 pounds (900 kg) and reaching anywhere from five to eight feet in length (2 m). Leatherbacks are the only sea turtle without a completely bony shell. Their carapace is best described as rubbery like a handball or tire sidewall. The world record leatherback was discovered in 1988, off the coast of Wales. It weighed nearly 2,020 pounds (915 kg).

550-2000 LBS

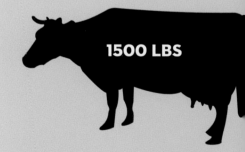

1500 LBS

80-100 LBS

60 LBS

Which sea turtle is the smallest?

The smallest sea turtle in the world is the Kemp's ridley, weighing between eighty to one hundred pounds (45 kg) and reaching a maximum of twenty-four to twenty-eight inches in length (60-70 cm). However, their smaller size does not limit their ability to travel thousands of miles during the course of their lifetime.

How deep can sea turtles dive?

All sea turtles are avid divers, and some dive deeper than whales. With the powerful force of their forelimbs and unique anatomy, they are able to descend hundreds of feet into the blue abyss. Leatherbacks are known to dive deeper than 4,000 feet. To put this in perspective, the Empire State Building stands at 1,250 feet. Triple its height, and that is how deep a leatherback can dive!

Do all sea turtle species travel long distances?

Migration is an ancient calling for these creatures, and sea turtles are known to travel thousands of miles in their lifetime. They are among the top five animals that migrate long distances. With their hydrodynamic shape enabling them to carve through the water with ease, sea turtles are built for efficient swimming. Their powerful forelimbs function like wings, while their back legs act as stabilizers and rudders. Leatherbacks and loggerheads are the two species that are believed to cover the greatest number of miles in their lifetime. The flatback is a bit of a "homebody," residing over Australia's continental shelf.

Is there an area where most sea turtle species can be found?

Sea turtles live in many places around the world, but the Atlantic Ocean is home to six of the seven species. The "Florida Five," consisting of the leatherback, loggerhead, green, hawksbill, and Kemp's ridley all use Florida's warm, rich waters as feeding grounds. Three of these species (leatherbacks, loggerheads, and greens) routinely nest along the Florida coast. All seven species roam and migrate. Scientists believe they are quite deliberate about targeting specific routes and geographical locations for foraging and nesting.

Are sea turtles smart?

Sea turtles have survived for millions of years, but it is unlikely that they did so by being smart. Sea turtles, like most animals, are capable of learning some things, but a lot of what they need to know for survival is "built in." For example, hatchlings instinctively know how to find the ocean when leaving the nest. Mature females must learn what beaches to return to when nesting for the first time by remembering some characteristic of that beach's location—most likely learned when hatchlings.

How long do sea turtles live?

These animals are among the elders of the ocean. It is believed that most sea turtles have the ability to live to approximately one hundred years of age, but in nature their life expectancy is much shorter because of disease, predators, or bad luck. Far too often sea turtles find themselves entangled in fishing lines, hooks, and nets. Longer life spans would be a reality for most turtles if worldwide fishing practices reduced bycatch—the unwanted marine life caught by mistake during commercial fishing. Unfortunately, sea turtles are commonly among those marine creatures caught, injured, or killed unintentionally.

up to 100 years

Can a sea turtle defend itself?

This is no easy task. Unlike tortoises and freshwater turtles, sea turtles cannot withdraw their head or limbs into their shell to protect themselves. Their hard shell (carapace and plastron) offers them some protection. Young sea turtles have been known to float, mimicking inanimate objects. Swimming fast, diving to great depths, making sharp, agile turns, and camouflage are other defense mechanisms used to flee the threat of predators. Adult leatherbacks and loggerheads are known to ram and bite attacking sharks. Finally, excellent olfactory and visual capabilities keep them keen to their surroundings, offering them an opportunity to escape when necessary. While many will not make it to adulthood, sea turtles are very resilient; some are lucky enough to heal from shark bites or other injuries.

What are the greatest threats to sea turtles?

The loss of critical nesting and feeding habitats are the greatest threats to these reptiles. In order to successfully nest, sea turtles must have access to protected beaches and natural sand, void of artificial light. Remember, no nests, no future for these animals. Sea turtles rely on healthy oceans, lush seagrass meadows, and thriving coral reefs in order to forage and maintain good health. In an effort to reduce sea turtle fatalities, fishing practices must still improve. The use of long lines, gillnets, and trawls still accidentally hook and entrap sea turtles. These cause life-threatening injuries and often prevent sea turtles from surfacing for oxygen—as a result, they are left to drown. Ghost nets (lost or abandoned netting) present a serious threat as well. Found in oceans worldwide, all sorts of marine life, birds, and invertebrates become fatally entangled. These nets often cause damage over the course of years before being removed or breaking down.

Are sea turtles in

ALL 7

FLATBACK Natator depressus • GREEN Chelonia mydas • HAWKSBILL Eretmochelys imbricata • KEMP'S RIDLEY Lepido

danger of extinction?

Six species are listed under the **U.S. Endangered Species Act.**
All sea turtle species are endangered worldwide, many critically.
Extinction (meaning "gone forever") is a real possibility for any of
the seven species unless there is better enforcement of U.S. and
international regulations. The time to act on behalf of all sea turtles
is now.

SPECIES

kempii • LEATHERBACK Dermochelys coriacea • LOGGERHEAD Caretta caretta• OLIVE RIDLEY Lepidochelys olivacea

When sea turtles come ashore to nest, how can we help them?

The best way to help a nesting sea turtle is to respect her need for a clean environment, privacy, and a quiet, dark space. Nesting areas should be viewed as sacred ground. Unfortunately, beaches are becoming more and more fragmented by seawalls and rock piles. Artificial lighting often disrupts sea turtles; this can repel females and confuse hatchlings. Litter and pollutants—such as sewage, plastics, and pesticides from nearby dwellings, marinas, docks, and other man-made facilities—can also impact the quality of nesting grounds. Participating in coastal clean-up efforts is one of the best ways to help protect the next generation of sea turtles; a clean environment is a "win-win" for everyone.

Why are sea turtles harvested in different parts of the world?

MEAT
FOOD SOURCE, PROTEIN, OIL, TURTLE SOUP

SKIN
LEATHER HANDBAGS, SHOES

EGGS
FOOD SOURCE, PROTEIN, SOCIAL CUSTOMS

SHELL
JEWELRY, ACCESSORIES

WHOLE TURTLE
TAXIDERMY MOUNTS FOR DISPLAYS

"When the BUYING stops, the KILLING can too."

WildAid

Why are sea turtles so vital to the well-being of this planet, and all of us?

Every living being on this planet, from the smallest plankton to the largest mammal, is part of a food chain and fragile ecosystem. By protecting sea turtles we reinforce the stability of the environment at large, thus protecting our own well-being. Coral reefs thrive because of sea turtles and the diverse marine life inhabiting that community. Sea turtles also promote the health and growth of seagrass meadows by acting as grazers. It's simple, healthy aquatic ecosystems are essential to our own survival. Remember, over fifty percent of the oxygen we breathe is produced by phytoplankton in the ocean.

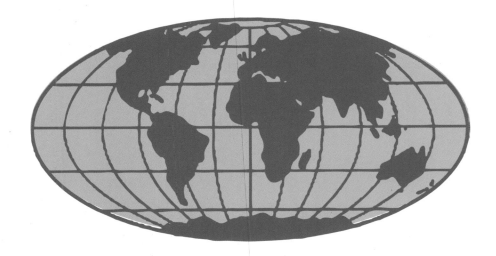

Why should people care about sea turtles?

Future generations rightfully deserve the pleasure of experiencing firsthand these magnificently beautiful animals. It is also important to recognize that sea turtles are an integral part of the ocean ecosystem that needs to be healthy in order for us all to thrive. Biodiversity exists in the ocean for a reason, and we are well advised to protect it. When we all act together to support the protection of sea turtles, their population thrives—this leads to a healthier and more interesting environment for us all to enjoy.

How can we all help to save sea turtles?

1. Abide by laws and efforts that seek to protect sea turtles and their natural habitats.

2. Avoid using plastic bags or helium balloons—sea turtles ingest this type of floating trash, sometimes mistaking it for food.

3. Support conservation organizations that address key threats to sea turtles.

4. Write or call legislators and encourage them to vote in favor of conservation efforts benefiting sea turtles and their habitats.

5. Use biodegradable products for lawn care, garden, and household tasks—these products end up in waterways that flow into the ocean.

6. **If you go to the beach during nesting months, please remove all beach chairs, umbrellas, and trash upon leaving. Flatten sand castles and fill in any holes formed on the beach.**

7. **Share the beach. Do not disrupt any roped off nesting grounds, especially where "NO TRESPASSING" signs are posted.**

8. **Respect artificial light-restriction laws near beaches where sea turtles nest.**

9. **Sign petitions that fight to stop accidental and intentional sea turtle deaths. Boycott all turtle products, both meat and fashion accessories.**

10. **Participate in an "ADOPT A SEA TURTLE" program through one of the many non-profits that offer this fun and easy way to help save sea turtles.**

Make a difference

1. Conservation International /www.conservation.org
2. Jean-Michel Cousteau's Ocean Future Society /www.oceanfutures.org
3. Loggerhead Marinelife Center /www.marinelife.org
4. Natural Resource Defense Council /www.nrdc.org
5. Oceana /www.oceana.org
6. Plant a Fish /www.plantafish.org
7. Sea Turtle Conservancy /www.conserveturtles.org
8. Seaturtle.org /www.seaturtle.org
9. Wildlife Conservation Society /www.wcs.org
10. WildAid /www.wildaid.org

"The future of SEA TURTLES is in OUR hands."

Jim Abernethy

Resources

Abernethy, Jim. Interview by author. Personal interview. West Palm, FL, October, 22, 2011.

Davis, Frederick Rowe. The Man Who Saved Sea Turtles. New York: Oxford University Press, 2007.

Gulko, DA, and KL Eckert. Sea Turtles: An Ecological Guide. Honolulu: Mutual Publishing, 2004.

Ripple, Jeff. Sea Turtles. Stillwater: Voyageur Press, 1996.

Safina, Carl. Voyage of the Sea Turtle. New York: Owl Books, 2007.

Salmon, Dr. Mike. Interview by author. Personal and email interview. Boca Raton, FL, October, 20, 2011.

Spotila, James R.. Sea Turtles. Baltimore: The Johns Hopkins University Press, 2004.

Witherington, Blair. Sea Turtles. St. Paul: Voyageur Press, 2006.

Wood, Larry. Interview by author. Email interview. Florida, August 23, 2011.

Wyneken, Dr. Jeannette. Interview by author. Personal and email interview. Boca Raton, FL, October, 20, 2011.

On-line Resources

Archi Carr Center for Sea Turtle Research
http://accstr.ifl.edu/newweb/index.shtml

Caribbean Conservation Corporation
http://www.cccturtle.org/aboutccc.php

Florida Atlantic University
http://www.science.fau.edu/biology/faculty/wyneken.html

Humane Society of the United States
http://www.humanesociety.org/

National Geographic
http://www.nationalgeographic.com/

National Oceanic and Atmospheric Administration
http://www.nmfs.noaa.gov/pr/species/turtles/

Natural Resource Defense Council
http://www.nrdc.org

Seaturtle.org
http://www.seaturtle.org

The Leatherback Trust
http://leatherback.org/

University of North Carolina at Chapel Hill
Kenneth Lohmann Lab
http://www.unc.edu/depts/geomag/

U.S. Fish and Wildlife Services
http://www.fws.gov/northflorida/SeaTurtles/seaturtle-info.htm

Photo Credits

 page 9   Jennifer R. Nolan

 page 53   Dr. Mike Salmon

 page 18   Chloe Schauble

 page 58   Matthew H. Godfrey

 page 19   Larry Wood

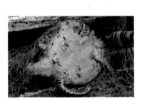 page 74   WildAid

 page 46   Hector Raul Chenge Alvarez

 page 82   WildAid

 page 47   Juana Antonia Torres

 All other images by Jim Abernethy